Sea Fright

Tony Bradman • Jon Stuart

Contents

OXFORD
UNIVERSITY PRESS

Macro Marvel
(billionaire inventor)

Welcome to Micro World!

Macro Marvel invented Micro World – a micro-sized theme park where you have to shrink to get in.

A computer called *CODE* controls Micro World and all the robots inside – MITEs and BITEs.

A MITE

A BITE

Disaster strikes!

CODE goes wrong on opening day.
CODE wants to shrink the world.

Macro Marvel is trapped inside the park ...

2

Enter Team X!

Four micro agents – *Max, Cat, Ant* and *Tiger* – are sent to rescue Macro Marvel and defeat CODE.

Mini Marvel joins Team X.

Mini Marvel
(Macro's daughter)

In the last book ...

* Max and Ant hid in a sunken ship to escape the Octo-BITE.

* They became trapped in a box of jewels.

* Cat and Tiger tracked them and came to their rescue.

**CODE key
(5 collected)**

You are in the Shark Dive zone.

3

Before you read

Sound checker

Say the sound.

se

Sound spotter

Blend the sounds.

n	oi	se

s	e	n	se

p	l	ea	se

s	t	e	p	s

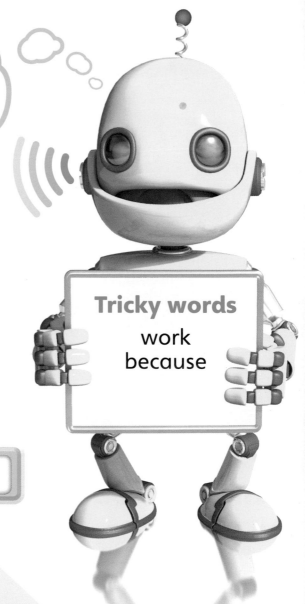

Tricky words

work
because

Into the zone

Team X and Mini are in the
Shark Sub. How do you think
they will get the CODE key?

The Plan

Welcome to the Shark Sub

"We need a good plan to get the CODE key from the Octo-BITE," said Max.

"We can make a plan on my Gizmo," said Mini.

Snorp! Snorp!

"Please don't make so much noise, Rex!" said Mini. "We need to work quickly."

Step 1

Tiger will swim near the BITE.
He must be as quiet as a mouse
so the BITE cannot hear him.

Step 2

Cat will swim round and round
to make a whirlpool.
This will confuse the BITE.

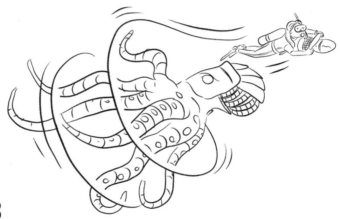

Step 3

Tiger will unscrew the CODE key.

"This plan makes sense because it has very clear steps," said Max. "Are you all ready?"

Now you have read ...
The Plan

Take a closer look

Read the split sentences explaining Team X and Mini's plan.
Can you join the right pieces together using the word 'so'?

Tiger needs to be quiet ...		... Tiger can get the CODE key.
Cat needs to swim fast ...	**so**	... she can make a whirlpool.
Cat needs to make a whirlpool ...		... the BITE cannot hear him.
The BITE needs to be confused ...		... the BITE gets confused.

Thinking time

What do you think of Team X and Mini's plan? Do you think
it will work? Is there anything that puzzles you?

We have a good plan!

11

Before you read

Sound checker
Say the sound.

se

Sound spotter
Blend the sounds.

t	ea	se

l	oo	se

m	ou	se

d	i	zz	y

Tricky word
because

Into the zone

What do you think the BITE will do?

Ink Attack!

Team X and Mini were ready to carry out the plan.

"I can't wait to tease this BITE," said Cat.

Tiger's watch glowed red because the BITE was near.

Tiger swam up to the BITE very carefully. He needed to be as quiet as a mouse.

Tiger waved to Cat to get to work.

Cat turned on her sea speeder and whizzed round and round. She made a huge whirlpool.

The BITE started spinning round.
It became dizzy and confused.

Tiger tried to unscrew the CODE key but it was too tight.

The BITE was angry now.
Its tentacles shot out to attack Tiger.
"Please, Cat! Help me," cried Tiger.

Together, Cat and Tiger twisted the key. It was nearly loose!

Now the BITE was really angry! It raised a tentacle and shot ink at Tiger. The blast of ink thrust Tiger backwards.

Tiger was hurt. Cat pulled him as they swam back to the Shark Sub. "We need to get you to Mini – and fast!" said Cat.

Now you have read ...
Ink Attack!

Text checker
Did Cat and Tiger stick to the plan?
What went wrong? What do you think
they could have done differently?

Thinking time
Which word did the author choose
to describe the BITE getting cross?

annoyed	grumpy
snappy	mad
irritated	angry

Read all the words that describe being cross.
Can you put them in order, starting with the
least cross and ending with the most cross?